EDGAR DEGAS

1834 — 1917

In aid of The
Police Dependants' Trust

4th June — 4th July, 1970

THE LEFEVRE GALLERY

THE POLICE DEPENDANTS' TRUST

Patron H.M. THE QUEEN

AN APPEAL BY LORD STONHAM, O.B.E.

Born of a tragedy which shocked a nation, the Police Dependants' Trust today holds out hope and a helping hand to the widows and children of the men who died protecting us.

Policemen are taken for granted. They are the familiar men in blue, daily seen on point duty or patrolling the streets of Britain's cities, towns and villages. But every year many die or are seriously injured safeguarding Mr. and Mrs. Average Citizen from fear of assault and loss and damage to property.

The Police Dependants' Trust Special Appeal provides an opportunity for everyone to show their gratitude and acknowledge in a practical way the immeasurable debt we owe to policemen and their families.

The brutal murder of three London policemen in Shepherd's Bush in 1966 evoked a wave of public anger and sympathy. Donations flowed in from all over the country for the families so cruelly left fatherless and husbandless.

But policemen get killed and badly injured in places other than Shepherd's Bush. Death or serious injury is an occupational hazard.

The Shepherd's Bush tragedy spotlighted the pressing need for a national permanent fund for policemen's dependants. With a generous donation of £100,000 from Sir William Butlin, the Police Dependants' Trust was born.

Today it provides the extras which make a difference to the quality of living of the women and children whose men have died or been incapacitated in the course of duty.

The Trust needs £1 million capital to remain a viable long term proposition. So far it has reached but half its target. Nobody can replace the losses suffered by policemen's families but can help to ease the financial burden which death or injury has caused.

The Rt. Hon. Lord Stonham, Minister of State at the Home Office, is Chairman of the Trust's Special Appeal Committee. Other members are Mrs. Ruth Adam, Lord Brecon, Sir William Butlin, Lord Cottesloe, Mr. Geoffrey Knight, Sir Edwin McAlpine, Sir John Ure Primrose, The Dowager Marchioness of Reading, Lord Sainsbury, Sir John Waldron and Lord Willis.

Acknowledgements

The Directors of the Lefevre Gallery wish to express their gratitude to those private collectors who have so generously consented to lend paintings or sculptures to this exhibition. Because the majority of lenders wish to remain anonymous, the collections from which the exhibition has been drawn have not been recorded in the catalogue, in the case of the pictures in public possession.

We would like to express our thanks to Mr. Paul and Mr. Philippe Brame without whose invaluable help and access to their records, this exhibition would not have been possible. Also to Messrs Arthur Tooth and Sons, Mr. Daniel Wildenstein, Mr. Leonard Foster, and to the officials at the Glasgow Art Galleries and Museum, the National Gallery of Scotland, Edinburgh, and the Walker Art Gallery, Liverpool, for their kind assistance and to Denys Sutton who prepared the catalogue.

Frontispiece. *Self-Portrait, c.* 1864. Drawing. The Louvre.

DEGAS BEHIND THE MASK

by Denys Sutton

Now that nineteenth-century French art is studied in such detail and with an increasing recognition of its connexions with the intellectual and social background, it is hardly surprising that greater attention is being paid to the work of Edgar Degas. It is significant that Camille Pissarro called him 'certainly the greatest artist of our epoch'. It is also understandable that there should be as much curiosity about his personality as about his art, for neither is easy of access. He enjoyed hiding behind a mask; he believed that 'what's underneath is no one's business' and, as he told his young friend Daniel Halévy, 'there must be a certain mystery. Works of art must be left with some mystery about them'.

Inevitably, there has grown up a Degas legend. What was his secret, if any, it may be asked. And what sort of man was he? Art historians scan the evidence with the same pertinacity as the literary critics do the facts about Henry James. Fortunately more material is available about Degas than might be supposed. A student of physiognomy may discover certain clues as to his character in the various portraits of him. For a start, there are the youthful self-portraits, which bring out his timidity and haughtiness; then there are the portraits of him by his friends—F. Mathey's drawing (Fig. I), for instance—and finally the photographs. Some of these are by Degas himself; others are snapshots taken in Paris or the country. One of the most famous (Fig. II), possibly by Sacha Guitry, shows Degas, as a true *boulevardier*, walking in the streets of Paris, a city he loved deeply. One of the most affecting is the photograph taken in 1915 in the garden of Bartholomé's house in the rue Raffet which presents him as a latter-day Homer, to use the description of the painter Jacques-Emile Blanche.

Besides the visual evidence, there are the written testimonies of the men and women who knew him, and, since he has often been billed as a misanthrope, as a figure almost from Molière, it is fascinating to find how many people wrote about him. These include Blanche, Mary Cassatt, Berthe Morisot, Halévy, Paul Lafond, George Moore, Rivière, Sickert and Paul Valéry, and their accounts present different and, at times, contradictory aspects of his personality. His letters, too, can prove most revealing, laconic though they often are, and George Moore even claimed that they possess an almost Balzacian quality.

Parisian life was the main inspiration of Degas's art, but he himself was not only a Parisian for he had Creole and Neapolitan relations. He spoke Italian fluently and in old age would still sing Neapolitan songs. The Neapolitan blood in his veins may well explain the undoubted theatrical streak in his nature, and Sickert, himself an actor, provides an entertaining account of Degas's relating the humours of London life. He was also an excellent mimic, as both Valéry and Edmond de Goncourt have reported. At times he embraced a role too heartily, as when he broke off relations with his Jewish and Protestant friends over the Dreyfus affair; but a vigorous consistency to a viewpoint in which he believed was typical of his character.

In one of his letters Degas refers to his cold heart, but he was exaggerating, for warmth keeps on breaking through. Although he fell out with his brother René, for having deserted his blind wife and children, he kept up with the rest of his family and this sense of family solidarity is surely a very Latin trait. No doubt his prickly carapace was designed to protect his sensitivity and vulnerability. Moore, for one, did not believe that Degas was quite such a curmudgeon as he liked to make out. This novelist who, for all his romancing about his time in Paris, had a good deal to report about artistic life there, told Halévy that 'For a reason unknown to himself, Degas—never did a more sensitive human nature breathe beneath our skies—took devilish pains to persuade the world that he was an old bear incapable of finding a friendly word for anyone. The exact opposite is the truth . . . a first-class writer, Balzac, for example, could write some pages about a man who cannot resist the temptation of adorning himself out of coquettrie, with the mask of an old bear'.

Fig. I. *Edgar Degas* by F. Mathey, *c.* 1882. Collection Mr. and Mrs. Paul Mellon

He was certainly complicated and difficult, but in this respect he was no different from many other artists, and Edmond de Goncourt, no mean connoisseur of neurosis, considered him 'a very troubled spirit'. Yet he must be seen in the perspective of his epoch. Much is made of his sharp witticisms at other people's expense, but sallies of this sort were common during his period; the pugnacity of contemporary writers may be grasped from reading their criticism—veritable duels in words—or, for that matter, the Goncourt *Journal*. In any case, Degas was so sharp-eyed that he could not resist the temptation of pointing out faults in others. He was a master of the delicate art of contempt.

Considerable speculation has taken place as to why he remained single; the view—a superficial one surely—has even been ventilated that as a young man he entertained homosexual yearnings; but this charge is one that is often levelled unjustly against a bachelor. Degas himself stated that he believed in marriage, even moaning his single state when he was in his 50s; however, he did stress that marriage was not for him, owing to his devotion to his art. The view that an artistic career and marriage are incompatible was widely held in his period, and the destructive force of an unsuitable match for a painter forms the theme of the brothers Goncourts' novel *Manette Salomon*. In fact, one may suspect that the obligations of matrimony, as opposed to its charms, proved hard to bear for many a nineteenth-century painter or writer; Zola and Dickens come to mind.

In his own case Degas may well have been right. He seems to have undergone some sentimental disappointments as a young man, for the *carnets* reveal that he was in love, but it is surprising that the Goncourts did not retail any tit-bits of gossip about him on this score. However Edmond does hint that Degas's sexual appetite was on the weak side. If, in later years, he had contemplated marriage, problems would have arisen. A man with his background, the upper bourgeoisie, could only have married someone from his own class, especially as he believed so strongly in its rules. There was never any question for him of love in a garret (the sort of life depicted in Zola's novel *L'Oeuvre*); marriage would have involved a proper household with staff and social obligations—*les corvées mondaines*. These would have placed a strain on his financial resources after 1874, for then he had to rally to the support of the family: Degas et Fils were in difficulties. It was characteristic of his sense of honour that he acted in this way; and it was no less so that during the 1870 war he reproved a friend who had sketched a dead comrade, instead of bringing his body back to the lines.

No real evidence in fact is available to suggest that Degas was an anti-feminist: he specifically referred to the graces of the local girls; knew his way to the *maisons closes*—as his monotypes prove; and his most splendid paintings, drawings and pastels celebrate the pleasures of contemplating the female body.

In early and middle years Degas had numerous friends and enjoyed dining with the Rouarts or the Halévys and visiting the Valpinçons at their country-home at Menil-Hubert in Normandy, which was close to Haras-le-Pin, a famous stud. He was on close terms with various artists—Bartolomé and Tissot, for example—and went on a trip to Madrid with the Italian painter Boldini. He liked listening to music at home—Lorenzo Pagans, the celebrated tenor and guitarist was a family friend—

Fig. II. *Edgar Degas, c.* 1910. Photograph possibly by Sacha Guitry. Bibliothèque Nationale, Paris.

or spending the evening at the opera or ballet. Gluck was a favourite composer and Daniel Halévy recalled that when one evening a woman pianist suggested playing a Beethoven sonata to him, Degas gently dissuaded her thus: 'When I hear a theme of Beethoven's I feel as though I were walking alone in a forest with all my troubles'.

When he grew older, melancholy plagued him, but the reasons for this are understandable. His eyesight, which had already troubled him in the 1870s, grew worse and in the final years he was practically blind, and thus cut off from working or reading. Under the circumstances it was hardly surprising that he should have been lonely and cantankerous. In addition, Valéry points out that Degas suffered from indigestion, and he describes dining with him off plain veal and macaroni followed by Dundee marmalade. One is often tempted to ask how much nineteenth-century spleen was due to abdominal troubles; Edmond de Goncourt, for instance, was often in bed with liver attacks, and these that can hardly have been exclusively psychosomatic and may have been caused by his habit of constantly dining out.

Degas's dissatisfaction was due not only to failing eyesight and the discomforts of old age but also to his conviction that the times were out of joint. He was born in 1834 and died in 1917, so he witnessed many changes; the 1848 Revolution, the Franco-Prussian War of 1870, the savagery of the Commune and then the establishment of the Third Republic, with what appeared to him its stench of corruption, and finally the 1914 War. In politics he was something of an innocent; so much is clear from Valéry's report of the artist's conversations with Clemenceau. Moreover, he was highly suspicious of the State's intervention in artistic matters; what would he have said if he had lived in our time! He had all the disdain of the high-principled *rentier* for the upstart; 'in my day one did not arrive' is one of his famous sayings. He made no secret of his views, declaring: 'Today everything is vulgarized, education and even art. Talk of popular art, what a criminal folly. As if the artists themselves did not have a hard enough time to find out about art, but it all comes from these modern ideas of equality ... In past times everyone stayed in his own place and dressed according to his own station; today the obscurest grocer's boy reads the

9

Fig. III. *La Famille Bellelei, c,* 1870. The Louvre.

newspapers and dresses like a gentleman . . . what an infamous century. The idea that all men are equal is infamous'.

The changes in Paris must have disturbed him too, and he was himself a victim of urban development, for, in later years, his house in the rue Victor-Massé (opposite the old Bal Tabarin) was sold over his head. A friend pointed out to him that he had the means to buy it himself, but Degas would not countenance such a proposition, for, like many old people, he felt harder up than circumstances justified. Perhaps there was also a touch of avariciousness in his character. Mrs. Havemeyer relates in her memoirs that, after agreeing to sell *The Collector of Prints* (now in The Metropolitan Museum, New York) to her and her husband for one thousand dollars, the artist asked them to leave it with him for a short time as he was anxious to make some minor improvements. After two years, he exacted from the Havemeyers three times the original price, explaining that his pictures had meanwhile increased in value. Not for nothing did he come from a banking family!

Nevertheless, it does not do to overdraw the picture of him as a misanthropic bear. Besides the judgment of Moore, which has already been quoted, it is as well to recall that Léonce Bénédite told Charles Ricketts in 1914 of 'a recent change in the character of Degas, his new friendliness and kindliness and love of simple pleasures, his hatred for his age and his regret of life'.

Degas's respect for tradition was as evident in his art as in his outlook. He did not consider that the depiction of the modern world in any way entailed a break with the past. It hardly requires emphasizing, in fact, that he was one of the most visually educated artists not only of his own day but of all time. His *carnets* in the Bibliothèque Nationale, Paris, which unfortunately have not yet been published in full, as they richly deserve to be, indicate the extensive range of his taste, as do the copies he painted after the Old Masters. He studied Classical art, as might be expected of someone who had been so well grounded in the Classics at school, and, more unexpectedly, he was interested in Assyrian art; he admired the early Italians—Giotto and Fra Angelico—and enthused over Botticelli; and he liked Signorelli and, so it would

10

Fig. IV. *Mendiante Romaine*, 1857. City Art Gallery, Birmingham.

appear, Piero della Francesca. He looked at Clouet and Holbein, the sixteenth-century Venetians, and Rembrandt; and Van Dyck meant much to him as well. His affection for the Pre-Raphaelites, for Piero and Signorelli, not to mention El Greco, placed him in the forefront of modern sensibility. However, his love of the Old Masters did not exclude his appreciating such contemporaries as Cézanne, Gauguin and Odilon Redon, and he praised the *fusains* of the last-named. Naturally, he favoured the work of Manet and his friends, de Nittis and Tissot.

His passion for art turned him into an inveterate collector and he formed a major collection of paintings, drawings and prints. His favourites were Ingres and Delacroix, a choice in some ways reflecting the twin poles of his own art —line and colour. He owned Ingres's portraits of the marquis de Pastoret, M. de Norvins and M. and Mme Leblanc, the full-length of the baron Schwiter by Delacroix, which is now in the National Gallery, London, and that artist's superb small picture of the duc de Morny's bedroom. Obviously, his private collection played some part in the formation of his style and it is worth underlining that he owned around 1,000 prints by Gavarni. Collecting became for him an obsession; he spared no pains to secure a piece on which he had set his heart.

Degas's eclectic taste led him to look for and to buy Oriental carpets, and, significantly, he once told his friend Jeanniot that when painting a picture he had remembered an Oriental rug that he had seen in the place de Clichy. 'You have got to make use of your memory', he declared. His interest in the rich yet delicate colours of Oriental textiles may well account for some of the colours in his later paintings. He was also a lover of Japanese art. These tastes indicate the way in which his painting reflects the exotic note that has so often intervened in French art, with the chinoiserie of the eighteenth century, with Delacroix and, nearer our own time, with Matisse.

Degas declared that 'they call me a painter of dancers, not understanding that for me the dancer has been a pretext for painting beautiful fabrics and rendering movements'. In this context the operative words are 'beautiful fabrics'. Like so many artists of the nineteenth century, he subscribed to the concept of '*L'art pour l'art*'. He was a hunter of aesthetic sensations and an amateur of elegant details. Typically he complained to Edmond de Goncourt that one no longer saw 'any sloping shoulders in society'. It was this writer who perceptively asked if Degas ever altogether achieved 'something absolutely complete'. This should not be taken to mean that he was unable to paint individual masterpieces, for that he certainly could, but that he was also a creator of fragments which, in the same way as the sculptural fragments of Rodin, derive part of their appeal from their explicit lack of finish. They must be seen in their own right. From one point of view, indeed, the art of Degas may be considered as the most subtle expression of that spirit of civilized dilettantism which was so brilliantly expressed in late-nineteenth- and early-twentieth-century Paris, a period when so many searchers after the rare and the exquisite flourished, men such as Metman, Koechlin and Albert S. Henraux, all collectors of Degas.

Degas's so evident enjoyment of the rare sensation does not mean that he fell into the trap of creating 'works of art' which were divorced from life; he once spoke

11

of taste as constituting a vice. Although some of the devices that he employed, such as the arabesque, are also found in Art Nouveau, his style was not artificial, but this is not to say that it was without artifice; on the contrary. In one respect Degas was very much in tune with the taste of his time—namely in his liking for women with long hair—and when we see his models combing their tresses we may well think of the famous scene in Debussy's opera where Pelléas caresses Mélisande's hair.

Degas quickly achieved mastery. His self-confidence is manifest in the superb early portraits, for, although he learnt much from Ingres, he soon evolved his own formulae, as in the discreet double-portrait of the Duke and Duchess of Morbilli (Museum of Fine Arts, Boston) and *La Famille Bellelei* (Louvre—Fig. III). The last gives some indication of his study of Van Dyck. The nineteenth century was significant for portrait-painting in France—Ingres, Delacroix and Millet are among the best known masters of this genre—and the psychological insight that began to be revealed in the novel—Balzac, Stendhal, Flaubert and the Goncourts—was paralleled by a related finesse in portraiture. It was in the 1850s and 1860s that Degas perfected his approach as a portrait-painter; his eye for nuances was as acute as that of a novelist, and, as Moore pointed out, 'He will watch the sitter until he learns all her or his tricks of expression and movement, and then will reproduce all of them and with such exact and sympathetic insight that the very inner life of the man is laid bare'. On the whole, his portraits were of members of his own world; and Dr. Jean Sutherland Boggs has suggested that *Mendiante Romaine* (City Art Gallery and Museum, Birmingham— Fig. IV) should be interpreted as a genre painting. All the same, it betrays the same sort of sympathy for the poor and aged that is to be discerned in Sickert's paintings of Venetians.

Since Miss Phoebe Pool's valuable study of Degas's history paintings, one which takes into account their artistic and intellectual background, it is possible to see in a fresh light such pictures as *Les jeunes filles Spartiates*, *Sémiramis Construisant Babylone*, *La Fille de Jephté* and *Scène de guerre de Moyen-Age; Les Malheurs de la ville d'Orléans* (Fig. V). She has brought out, for instance, his deep love of the Classics, for it is claimed that he still enjoyed Theocritus and Horace in the original in his old age. 'Degas', she writes, 'was linked with the Hellenists of the eighteenth century, who regarded Greece not as a stern, abstract world peopled by Davidian statues, but by a young vital, civilisation full of freshness and energy. They preferred the early, more primitive Greece to the late Hellenistic world'. However, it is worth pointing out that later on a drawing of Madame Rouart and Hélène appears to have its prototype in a Hellenistic figurine.

The many drawings he did for *Sémiramis* or for *Les Malheurs de la ville d'Orléans* are of superlative quality; his studies of nudes for the latter picture can be placed alongside the marvellous sheets of the Renaissance. It is now more than ever recognized that the period which Degas spent in Italy was fundamental for the development of his art, but not only on account of the varied experiences that came his way— he saw Pompeian mosaics and painting at Naples—but also because his friendship with Gustave Moreau helped him to achieve richer colours. It was while in Florence, moreover, that Degas came into touch at the Caffé Michelangiolo with the Macchiaoli group, who were exponents of Realism.

The *carnets* establish that by the late-1850s Degas had begun to realize that history-painting was not the style best suited to him; his keen intelligence presumably made him aware that it could well lead him into a *cul-de-sac*. He became one of those painters who were increasingly captivated by the representation of urban existence— by the slice of life, in fact. In so becoming he was in step with the contemporary literary movement.

As yet there has not been a thorough examination of the reasons which induced Degas to adopt a Realistic attitude. The components of his style are more complex than they might seem at first sight. It would be fascinating to know to what extent Gavarni, so much admired by the Goncourts as well as by Degas, counted for something in his determination to depict Parisian life; not that he adopted the rather anecdotic, illustrative style of this artist. Degas is also known to have appreciated the German painter Alfred Menzel, painting a copy after his *The Ball* which is now in the Musée des Beaux-Arts, Strasbourg; and significantly Duranty was an admirer of

Fig. V. *Scène de Guerre de Moyen-Age, Les Malheurs de la Ville d'Orléans,*
The Louvre.

Menzel, as well as a close friend of Degas. Moreover, the relations between Degas and his two colleagues Tissot and Alfred Stevens require investigation. Then there is the intriguing question of his appreciation of English art; in 1872 he specifically asked Tissot to give his regards to Millais, even though they had not met, writing 'tell him of my appreciation for him.' He may have seen modern English painting at the Exposition Universelle of 1855 or at the Salon and he demonstrably studied English sporting prints, for one by J. F. Herring is seen in *Bouderie* (Metropolitan Museum, New York (Fig. VI)). Literature may also have contributed to his development; and it has been alleged that the so-called *Le Viol* in the Henry McIlhenny Collection, Philadelphia, is inspired either by Duranty's novel *Les Combats de Françoise Duquesnoy* or by Zola's novel, *Madeleine Férat*.

Degas may have also picked up Baudelaire's essay on Constantin Guys (1846), in which the poet had first expressed his belief that an artist should find his subject-matter in modern life. This was a view which was much in the air, for Edmond and Jules de Goncourt had savaged the history and neo-Classical painters in their reviews of the Salons of 1852 and 1855 and championed the thesis that landscape was the triumph of modern art.

Whatever reasons may have prompted him to become a painter of modern life, the pictures that resulted depict many of the experiences that then formed the normal programme of the man about town—visits to the racecourses, (see Fig. VII), the Opéra, (see Fig. VIII), the café-chantants and the brothel. Is it just possible that importance may be attached to Degas's love of *The Thousand and One Nights*? Did he see himself as a modern counterpart of Haroun al Raschid? His pictures enshrine the existence of the leisured classes of his day. And when he stopped to paint washerwomen at work or a scene in a café (Fig. IX) he was doing no more than many a *flâneur* who is arrested by what he sees going on around him, but the difference was that Degas gave artistic form to his observations. But there was nothing moralistic about such scenes, even though he had studied Hogarth, as the *carnets* show.

He was ever at pains to emphasize by precept and practice that the creation of a work of art was not a casual business, stating 'You must do over the same subject ten times, a hundred times. In art nothing must appear accidental; even a movement'. He was then a painter who worked from memory, from notes and from squared drawings. His belief in Realism was strong, and he wrote to Tissot in 1874 that 'The realist movement no longer needs to fight with the others; it already exists, it must show itself as something distinct, there must be a salon of realists'. Yet his Realism did not mean that he accepted the principles of Impressionism. Although his painting *Henri Valpinçon and Nurse, c.* 1871-72 (private collection), is a typical Impressionist

Fig. VI. *Bouderie, c.* 1874-76. The Metropolitan Museum, New York.

composition, Degas himself did not practise *plein-airisme*—art is not a sport was his view—and his few landscapes were done from memory. It is typical of his approach that the majority of his pictures of the racecourse are generalized; for instance, the racing colours of the jockeys cannot be identified.

Nevertheless, a more impressionistic and sketchy handling of paint may be observed in such notable portraits of the 1870s as those of Duranty (Glasgow Art Gallery, Fig. X) and Diego Martelli (National Gallery of Scotland), and the difference between these works and the more sombre portraits of the previous decade is noticeable. In both portraits, light and space are employed to emphasize the sitter's personality; they possess an acuteness which explains why Valéry detected a Stendhalien element in Degas's concept of line.

How brilliantly Degas succeeded in his aims, of discarding superfluities, of giving his works a stark formal discipline and of finding an individual colour is apparent when his pictures are compared with those of the countless painters—de Nittis, Raffaëlli and Jean Béraud, for example—who described the bric-à-brac of Parisian life. But Degas did not suppress human sympathy, whatever he may have said to the contrary. Take, for instance, his celebrated pictures of the ballet. Inevitably the subject-matter meant that the emphasis was usually placed on movement and colour. However, Degas also makes us aware of the individualities of the protagonists—of the *maître de danse* (possible M. Plugne) in *La Répétition de Danse* (No. 2), or of the three dancers who appear in a diagonal line in one of his most satisfactory pastels (No. 4).

He had studied the ballet so deeply and had memorized the salient details of performances or rehearsals so well that he knew just how to render them in his pictures and he could capture the excitement which occurs when the prima ballerina takes her bow or the expectancy that prevails when the *corps de ballet* musters and limbers up before the curtain rises (No. 19).

Before Degas's time, other painters, Watteau or Lancret for instance, had painted dancers or dance scenes, but, for all the delicacy of colour or psychological nuance

14

Fig. VII. *Le Faux Depart, c.* 1869-71. Collection Mr. and Mrs. John Hay Whitney.

that may be discerned in their works, their pictures do not possess the extraordinary authenticity of his depictions of the ballet. Is it ever possible to see the ballet without calling to mind his vision? This illusion of reality largely arises from his mastery of space, and, as Max Lieberman, the German painter, so rightly said, 'he composed not only in space but with space.' The figures are at home; they try out their exercises or flash across the stage, and that they do so effortlessly in his pictures is due to the fact that every action has been premeditated by the master, and, as Kleist emphasized in a famous essay, marionettes may be felt to perform more perfectly than actors. His outlook was that of a Classical master; he once declared: 'No art was ever less spontaneous than mine. What I do is the result of reflection and study of the great masters; of inspiration, spontaneity, temperament—temperament is the word —I know nothing'. In his ballet scenes, his calculation of relationships and observation of tonal interplay hark back to the great Dutch genre masters of the seventeenth century, to Vermeer and Terborch. There is too a puzzling passage in Edmond de Goncourt's account of his visit to the artist's studio, for he writes: '*Puis conçoit-on que dans ses reproductions si délicatement senties d'êtres et de natures, au lieu de mettre à cela le rigoureux décor du Foyer de la Danse de l'Opéra, il fasse dessiner par un perspecteur des architectures de Panini?*' There would seem to be little doubt that Degas studied earlier textbooks on perspective and William Wells in a fascinating analysis of the staircase in *La Répétition de Danse* (No. 20) has suggested that the artist may have recourse to such a treatise as that by Hans Vredeman de Vries (edition of 1633) or another of a similar nature 'in order to thoroughly master the complex problems of perspective which faced him' and that the staircase itself may be based on a model in his possession.

The study of Degas's sources is an intriguing subject. One feels that he was often haunted by the Antique. In a picture such as *La Répétition d'un ballet* in the Louvre, the use of *camaieu* produces an effect reminiscent of Classical sculpture. In a famous picture, which once belonged to Max Lieberman, and is now in the Cleveland Museum, Ohio, a dancer is shown in four different positions tying her ribbons. Undoubtedly

Fig. VIII. The Ballet Scene from Meyerbeer's '*Roberto il Diavolo*', 1876. Victoria and Albert Museum.

photography had something to do with the composition but the effect is that of a frieze. A similar impression is made by the celebrated picture, which was formerly owned by Sir William Eden, of washerwomen carrying baskets of linen and by some of the equestrian scenes.

Degas had a sharp eye for what was going on around him. He quickly understood the merit of the Japanese print which began to be so deeply appreciated in Paris in the 1850s and 1860s. Julius Meier-Graefe in his interesting, if in some respects critical, volume on Degas remarked that it seemed to him most appropriate that when a visitor visited the superb group of Degases belonging to comte Isaac de Camondo in his house near the Opéra, a room hung with fine Japanese prints had to be traversed. He felt that these pieces admirably complemented those of the French artist. It was Degas's keen study of such works—above all of the angles of vision that they presented—that explains some of the effects in his own pictures, in the *Place de la Concorde* (Louvre) for example. Meier-Graefe even went so far as to claim that it was his appreciation of the Japanese print that permitted Degas to discard what, in this critic's eyes, was the painter's academism. He wrote: 'In his most mature period he attained to the understanding of the recessions of planes, not as Manet and Monet did, not as a painter, but as a draughtsman, and in this way he absorbed in his own way one of the peculiarities of the Japanese, which has ever since been the red thread that passes through the history of European art; and it was by this means that he carried his eventful career to success.'

Since 1920, when Meier-Graefe's volume was published, more has been found out about Degas's deep interest in, and use of, photography. He was himself a keen amateur photographer and was one of the first men to own a Kodak in France. He enjoyed grouping figures to form a composition which he would then photograph—a practice later emulated by Vuillard. It was an indication of the theatrical touch in his personality that he should have found such pleasure in doing so. In practical terms his study of instantaneous movement produced considerable consequences for his art, for his portrait-painting and, more significantly, for his composition. Dr. Aaron

Fig. IX. *Au Café, c.* 1877-80. Fitzwilliam Museum, Cambridge.

Scharf has summed up the influence of photography on Degas very skilfully in his excellent book, *Art and Photography* (1968), writing 'Degas's singular attitude to one of the most firmly established and tenacious conventions in Western art, the system of rational perspective, may well be ascribed to photography. His frequent use of looming *repoussoirs* in the foregrounds of his pictures and the dwarfing of objects slightly farther in depth is sometimes said to have been inspired by Japanese prints. But the kind of perspective scale typical of a large number of his paintings and drawings springs, most likely in the first instance, from so-called aberrations of the photographic image'. His ambition 'to simulate the appearance of a single, animated figure recorded in more or less consecutive phases of its movement' even antedates the photographs of Major Eadward Muybridge but his knowledge of the famous photographs of horses in movement by Muybridge permitted him to represent this animal 'in the accurate positions of instantaneous photographs'. Degas was not the only artist to be interested in the precise definition of the movement of horses, and Edmond de Goncourt reports an interesting statement by Gavarni on this topic.

Degas's interest in what happens when the central axis is broken by movement, although the form remains contained by the contour, might be considered a shade paradoxical in view of his social and political views, in which adherence to the *status quo* was all important. Perhaps it was an expression of the *esprit contradictoire* in his nature. Moreover, Valéry noted that his Neapolitan ancestry gave him an inborn love of gesture. Dr. Boggs has suggested that in certain of his later works he was even keen to render psychological states and she instances his pastels of Louis Rouart and his wife, the daughter of Henri Lerolle, the musician. She notes that André Gide suspected tension in the Lerolle marriage and this she claims can be found in the gestures given to the pair by Degas. (See Figure XI.) Be this as it may, there can be little doubt that such a shrewd and even cynical observer of life as Degas would have been just the man to detect problems in the *ménage* of such close friends as the young Rouarts, if they existed.

Fig. X. *Portrait of Edmond Duranty,* 1879. Burrell Collection, Glasgow Art Gallery and Museum.

    His curious and questing mind inevitably led Degas to study the problems of technique. He was most resourceful in this respect, and the nature of the experiments that he made with different media can be followed from Denis Rouart's valuable book on this subject. He was especially fascinated by pastel. Why this particular medium should have appealed so strongly to French artists is not altogether clear; Leonardo da Vinci even claimed that it was an invention of the French School. In any event, French artists have produced over the years a superb series of pastels, and those by Degas may be placed in the tradition of La Tour and Perronneau. When he was a young man his father took him to see the collections of Dr. La Caze and Marcille, which were rich in examples of the eighteenth century, and he himself owned pastels by La Tour and Perronneau. His own pastels can be of remarkable elegance and charm. He was fortunate, too, in so far as he was able to learn from the painter Chialiva (a portrait of whom by Degas is in the Musée Bonnat, Bayonne) a method of fixing pastel. This has meant that the glitter of his colour has been preserved. It was a procedure that was followed by Vuillard, but the secret is now apparently lost.

    It was Degas's intense curiosity into ways and means that turned him into one of the most original graphic artists of the day. His monotypes have long been savoured by lovers of Degas, but it is only since the exhibition of a large group at the Fogg Museum, Cambridge, Massachusetts, and the publication of Miss Janis's check-list (1968) that his skill in this medium has become more widely realized. The monotype was first used by the Genoese painter Castiglione in the seventeenth century. Degas did not care for the term 'monotype' to describe a process to which he was introduced by the vicomte Lepic. It would be outside the confines of this essay to provide a detailed account of Degas's monotypes, and the reader may be referred to the admirable introduction by Miss Janis to the Fogg Museum publication and to that by Douglas Cooper for the exhibition held at the Lefevre Gallery in 1958. Yet one passage from Miss Janis's book must be quoted, for in it she makes the point that the artist's main reason for taking up the monotype medium seems to have been to prolong the flexible unfinished stage of the sketch: 'as he originally learned the technique from

Fig. XI. *M and Mme Rouart,* 1904. Pastel. Present whereabouts unknown.

Lepic, monotype required only a metal plate, ink and a rag. Thus the making of lines could be eliminated from the beginning. Monotype in the dark field manner forced him to concentrate on broad general shapes, and to consider structure and design exclusive of line at the most formative stage. Smearing the ink round and wiping it away, Degas began to compose broad patterns of light and shadow as well, and to incorporate these patterns into the composition structure rather than treat them simply as representational overlays'. He even used his own finger-prints to grey the black and white contrasts and, on some occasions, when the monotype was pulled from the plate, he added pastel; in other words, it was a medium which enabled him to engage in all sorts of fascinating experiments. Some of his most intriguing monotypes were of landscape and resulted from his trip to Burgundy with Bartholomé in 1890: these have the thrilling delicacy of a verse by Mallarmé.

Many of his most astonishing monotypes were of *maisons closes.* Some writers have suggested that they show disgust with human nature and with women especially, but this interpretation is arguable. The brothel was then an accepted part of life and Degas treats of its inmates with a degree of detachment, but also with a certain humour. It is only necessary to turn over the leaves of the sketchbook (See Figure XII), which he would use when dining at the Halévys', to be convinced that the humorous side of his nature could appear in his art as well as in his conversation.

Degas's passion for technical experiments and his concern with the exploration of form found further and magnificent expression in his sculpture; and as his eyesight worsened it was easier for him to model than to paint. He used a variety of media, clay, plasticine and wax, and the studies of dancers in movement or horses that resulted are brilliant and versatile. During his lifetime only one piece was shown publicly— the famous dancer in her tutu which was included in the Impressionist exhibition of 1881 and was praised by Whistler among others. After his death many pieces were found in his studio and some were cast in the lost-wax process by A. Hébrard. It was no mean feat owing to their condition; Degas had undergone considerable difficulties with the armatures.

The development of Degas's art over the years—and his life was a long one— illustrates how fruitfully he was able to renew himself. His themes may often have been the same, but not their treatment, and a longer account than is possible here would be required to indicate the changes that took place in his approach. As much as anything else, the depth of his vision may be seen in the many studies of the female nude that date from the later period. In the 1850s he had already made beautiful drawings of the nude for the *Malheurs de la ville d'Orléans,* studies that have a touch of Delacroix about them, and in the 1870s he represented the nude in his monotypes. (See No. 5.)

There was nothing at all self-conscious about his rendering of the nude. Moore reported him as once saying that he depicted '*la bête humaine qui s'occupe d'elle-même;*

Fig. XII. A page from the Halévy sketch-book.

une chatte qui se lèche'. Hitherto, Degas continued, 'the nude has always been represented in poses which presuppose an audience, but these women of mine are honest,
simple folk, unconcerned by any other interests than those involved in their physical
condition . . . It is as if you looked through a key-hole'. A good deal has been made
of Degas's reference to a key-hole, and it has been suggested that there is an element
of voyeurism in his pictures of the nude. Yet there is nothing at all unhealthy about
such works; besides their considerable formal and colouristic appeal, they possess a
radiant eroticism of an almost dreamlike quality; they pay yet another tribute to the
delicious possibilities and comforts of the female body. Whatever motives may have
prompted their execution, it is the result that counts. They may be placed in a noble
tradition, one embracing Titian and Rubens, and, despite Degas's insistence on the
animality in his women, they never lose their human qualities.

Lord Clark is surely correct in calling Degas the greatest draughtsman since the
Renaissance, but the immense attraction of Degas's drawings at times has tended to
occasion a lack of estimation of the colour values in the later works. He achieved
astonishing radiance in the pastels, juxtaposing most unusual tonalities, as in his
studies of Russian dancers performing the *kopak*, which date from 1895.

Max Raphael considered Degas to be an exponent of late-nineteenth-century
capitalism, arguing that 'Degas saw only one solution for the artist to withdraw into
solitude, to spit his disgust with the world in the face of God "our Father", from
which he created art, to sing for a moment'. This is an ingenious explanation, but it
does not do justice to a complex and remarkable genius who stamped his vision on
so many aspects of life. His character may have been tinged with the pessimism of
the *fin de siècle*, but in terms of artistic creation, which is what counts, there was
nothing pessimistic about his contribution; his solution of so many different technical
problems, his apprehension of form, his exquisite colour and, not least, the sense of
energy that radiates from his art and makes it so life-enhancing; all these attributes
have a nobility and charm that are perpetually refreshing.

Catalogue

Abbreviations

Atelier Degas—Ventes Atelier Degas, Galerie George Petit, Paris, 1st sale, May 6-8, 1918; 2nd sale, December 11-13, 1918; 3rd sale, April 7-9, 1919; 4th sale, July 2-4, 1919.

Lemoisne—Paul André Lemoisne, *Degas et son oeuvre,* 4 vols. 1947-49. All the items in the exhibition which appear in Lemoisne's Catalogue are illustrated.

Rewald—John Rewald, *Degas Works in Scripture. A Complete Catalogue,* 1944.

1 TROIS FEMMES ASSISES

Canvas: $8\frac{3}{4} \times 10\frac{3}{4}$ in. (22.2 $\times$ 27.3 cm)

Colls: G. Pellet, Paris; Maurice Exsteens, Paris; Klipstein and Kornfeld, Berne; Alastair Roger

Exh: Berne, Klipstein and Kornfeld *'Choix d'une Collection Privée'*, 1960 (No. 9, repr.); London, The Lefevre Gallery, 'XIX and XX Century French Pictures', April, 1961 (No. 4, repr.)

Painted *c.* 1865.

No. 1

2   LA REPETITION DE DANSE

Canvas: $27\frac{3}{4} \times 32\frac{1}{2}$ in. (69.2 $\times$ 82.5 cm)
Signed lower left

Colls: Jacques-Emile Blanche, Paris; Sir William Burrell, Scotland

Exh: Amsterdam, 1922, '*Cent Ans de Peinture Française*' (No. 48); Paris, 1924, Galerie Georges Petit, 'Degas' (No. 48); London, 1932, Royal Academy, 'French Art' (No. 481).

Lit: ? Edmond de Goncourt, *Journal, Mèmoires de la Vie Littèraire*, ed. R. Ricatte, 1956, X, p. 164; G. Grappe in *L'Art et le Beau*, I, 1911, repr. p. 47; L. Hourticq in *Art et Décoration*, 1912, repr. p. 100; Paul Lafond, *Degas*, 1918-19, I, repr. p. 151; J. Meier-Graefe, *Degas*, 1920, pl. XXX; A. Vollard, *Degas*, 1924, repr. p. 118; J. B. Manson, *The Life and Works of Edgar Degas*, 1927, pl. 31; *Kunst and Künstler*, 1932, repr. p. 12; C. Mauclair, *Degas*, 1937, repr. p. 126; P. Jamot, *Degas*, 1939, pl. 38; Marguerite Rebatet, *Degas*, 1944, pl. 83; R. H. Wilenski, *Degas*, 1945, pl. 5; L. Browse, *Degas Dancers*, 1949, pl. 34. p. 347; Lemoisne, II, No. 430; Pierre Cabanne, *Degas*, 1960, pl. 80; F. Novotny, *Painting and Sculpture in Europe 1780-1880*, 1960, pl. 168, p. 199; K. Roberts in *Burlington Magazine*, CV, June, 1963, pp. 280-81; Phoebe Pool, *Degas*, 1963, pl. 34; William Wells in *Scottish Art Review*, 1964, 9 (3) pp. 14 ff.

Various drawings connected with No. 2 appeared in the Degas Sales, Lot 356, 2nd Sale, Lots 146, 362(2); 3rd Sale, Lot 272(a), 4th Sale. The classroom is in the opera house, Rue Le Peletier. The *Mère* on the extreme right is Sabine Neyt, Degas's housekeeper. The *maître de danse* is probably M. Plugne. The dancers are executing an arabesque.

Keith Roberts has suggested that No. 2 is identifiable with the picture which Edmond de Goncourt saw in the artist's studio, on 13th February, 1874, and that it was either finished or in an advanced state by that date. There is a less finished version in the Corcoran Gallery, Washington. (Lemoisne No. 398).

William Wells has put forward the suggestion that the staircase might be based on a wooden model (such as Degas was known to possess) and that he may have looked at a volume on the theory and practise of perspective such as the 1633 edition of Hans Vredemar de Vries's *Perspectiva Theoretica ac Practica*.

Lent by the Burrell Collection, Glasgow Art Gallery and Museum.

No. 2

3 FEMME METTANT SES GANTS

Oil on canvas: 24 × 18½ in. (60.9 × 46.9 cm.)

Facsimile signature stamp of Degas sale lower right.

Colls: Atelier Degas, 1st sale (Lot 55, repr): Georges Viau, Paris; Wildenstein, Paris; Mr. and Mrs. James Thrall Soby, Hartford, Connecticut; Private collection, U.S.A.

Lit: *L'Amour de l'Art*, September, 1925, (No. 9). repr. p. 370; Paul Jamot, *Degas*, 1939, pl. 39; Lemoisne, II, No. 438; Jean Sutherland Boggs, *Portraits by Degas*, 1962, Fig. 85 (repr. in colour).

Painted *c*. 1877.

No. 3

4 TROIS DANSEUSES EN LIGNE DIAGONAL SUR LA SCENE

Pastel: 24¾ × 19¾ in. (62.8 × 50.1 cm)
Signed upper right

Colls: Barrett Decap, Biarritz; Charles Bignou, Paris; Reid and Lefevre, London

Exh: Glasgow and London, Lefevre Gallery 'Works by Degas', June, 1928 (No. 7); London, Lefevre Gallery 'Degas', May-June, 1950 (No. 6, repr.)

Lit: Lemoisne, II, No. 701; L. Browse, *Degas Dancers*, 1949, pl. IX, pl. 134, p. 382; L. Browse in *Apollo*, LXXXV, February, 1967, pl II

Painted *c.* 1882. According to L. Browse, the two dancers at the bar are doing *pliés à la sécour;* the one in front is in *position allongée en quatrième ouverte.*

No. 4

5 FEMME A SA TOILETTE

Pastel over monotype: 11 $\times$ 14$\frac{15}{16}$ in. (28 $\times$ 38 cm)

Facsimile signature stamp of Degas sale lower left

Colls: Atelier Degas, 3rd Sale (Lot 408, repr.), René de Gras; Paul Brame, Paris

Lit: Lemoisne, II, No. 623; Eugenia Parry Janis, *Degas Monotypes*, 1968. No. 153, repr.

Executed 1880-85. No. 4 is the first of two impressions; see Janis No. 154 (repr.).

No. 5

6   FEMME NUE, DEBOUT
   Drawing: 23¼ × 18¼ in. (60.3 × 46.3 cm)
   Facsimile signature stamp of Degas sale upper left

Colls: Atelier Degas, 3rd sale (Lot 389, repr.)

Lit: Rewald, p. 100

A study for *Danseuse regardent la plante de son pied droit* (No. 29), Rewald, XLV. A. Hébrard made a plaster cast of this figure in *c.* 1900 but the wax model and thus the drawing were probably made several years before, at some date after 1888. The bronze is included in this exhibition as No. 30.

No. 6

7 FEMME AU TUB
Pastel: 26¼ × 26¼ in. (67.9 × 67.9 cm)
Signed upper right

Colls: Henri Lerolle, Paris

Exh: Paris, Musée de L'Orangerie, 'Degas', 1937 (No. 119); London, Wildenstein, 'The Kessler Collection', 1948 (No. 4); Edinburgh and London (Arts Council), 'Degas', 1952 (No. 19)

Lit: Lemoisne, III, No. 738

Painted *c.* 1883. Lemoisne points out that it may be compared with II, Nos. 1334, 1335, 1335 (1st) and Lot 294 in the 4th Atelier Degas Sale.

No. 7

8   LA TOILETTE

Pastel: 25 × 19¼ in. (63.5 × 48.8 cm)

Signed upper left

Colls: Tadamara Hayashi, Paris; Manzi, Paris; E. Blot, his sale, Paris, 5. 1900 (Lot 186 repr.); E. Blot, his sale, Paris, 10-5, 1906 (Lot 92 repr.); Kelekian, Paris; Arthur Tooth and Sons, London; Joseph Brochier, Lyons; Paul Rosenberg, New York

Exh.   Lyons, Palais St. Pierre, '*L'Impressionisme à nos Jours*', May, 1942 (No. 8)

Lit: Camille Mauclair, *Degas*, 1937, repr. p. 91; Lemoisne, II, No. 749

Painted *c*. 1883.

No. 8

9 DANSEUSE SE DEGOURISSANT LE BRAS DERRIERE LE DOS
A LA BARRE

Pastel: 43½ × 23½ in. (110.4 × 59.6 cm)
Facsimile signature stamp of Degas sale lower left

Colls: Atelier Degas, 1st Sale, (Lot 241, repr.); Jacques Seligmann, Paris; Duncan Phillips, Washington

Exh: London, Wildenstein, 'The French Impressionists and some of their Contemporaries', 1963 (No. 15, repr.)

Lit: L. Browse, *Degas Dancers,* 1949, Plate 219; Lemoisne, III. No. 811; *The Connoisseur,* January, 1960, pp 2, 5.

Painted *c.* 1884-88. No. 9 is a study for the painting in the Duncan Phillips Memorial Gallery, Washington (Lemoisne No. 807). For a drawing connected with this picture, see 1st Atelier Degas Sale (Lot 332 repr.). Cf. also Lemoisne II, Nos. 808, 819, 810 and 812.

No. 9

10 WOMAN IRONING

Canvas: 31½ × 25 in. (80 × 63.5 cm)

Facsimile signature stamp of Degas sale lower right

Colls: Atelier Degas, 1st Sale, (Lot 32 repr.); Georges Viau, Paris; César M. de Hauke, New York; Jacques Seligmann, New York; Wildenstein, Paris; The Hon. Mrs. A.E. Pleydell-Bouverie. Bought by the Walker Art Gallery, Liverpool, in 1968 from the estate of the late Mrs. Pleydell-Bouverie under the terms of the Finance Act 1930 with the aid of contributions from the National Art-Collections Fund (Eugene Cremetti Fund), The Victoria and Albert Museum Grant Fund and the Gallery's Special Appeal Fund.

Exh: New York, Jacques Seligmann, 'Courbet to Seurat', March-April, 1937 (No. 7); London, National Gallery, 'Nineteenth Century French Paintings', 1942 (No. 37); Edinburgh Festival and London, Tate Gallery (Arts Council), 'Degas', 1952 (No. 22); London, Tate Gallery, 'The Pleydell-Bouverie Collection', 1954 (No. 15); London, Tate Gallery, 'Private Views', 1963 (No. 152)

Lit: Waldemar George in *L'Amour de l'Art*, September, 1929 (No. 9), repr. p. 365: Lemoisne, 11, No. 846: R. H. Wilenski, *Degas*, 1945, pl. L8; Pierre Cabanne, *Degas*, 1960 (No. 10), pp. 116-17

Painted *c.* 1885 and described by Lemoisne as *Repasseuse à Contre Jour*. There are two other *Repasseuses à Contre Jour* very close to this picture; one (Lemoisne, No. 356) is in The Metropolitan Museum, New York (H.Q. Havemeyer Collection, No. 29. 100. 46) and dates from *c.* 1874; the other (Lemoisne, II, No. 685) is in the collection of Mme Georges Durand-Ruel and was painted in 1882. For a note on Degas's treatment of washer women and ironers, see P. Cabanne, *op. cit.* No. 10 pp. 116-17.

Lent by the Walker Art Gallery, Liverpool.

No. 10

11 DANSEUSE AU TUTU VERT

Pastel: $18\frac{1}{2} \times 13$ in. (46.9 $\times$ 33 cm)

Signed lower right

Coll: Pierre Bonnard, 1st sale, Paris 23-2 1954 (Lot 37)

Painted *c.* 1887.

No. 11

12 AVANT LA COURSE

Pastel: $32\frac{1}{2} \times 40\frac{1}{2}$ in. (82.5 $\times$ 102.8 cm)

Facsimile signature stamp of Degas sale lower left

Colls: Atelier Degas, 1st sale, (Lot 154, repr.); Trotti, Paris; Winkel & Magnussens, Copenhagen; Durand-Ruel, Paris; Etienne Bignou, Paris; Reid and Lefevre, London

Exh: New York, 'Paintings and Drawings by Degas', 1928; London, Wildenstein, 'The Kessler Collection', 1948 (No. 5); Edinburgh and London, 1952 (Arts Council); 'Degas', 1952 (No. 24)

Lit: Ragnar Hoppe, *Degas*, 1922, repr. p. 62; Lemoisne, III, No. 939

Painted *c.* 1888. Several drawings connected with No. 12 appeared in the Degas sales, 3rd Sale, Lots 89 (2), 90 (24), 98 (1), and 4th Sale, Lot 383 (a). See also a pastel, Lemoisne, III, No. 1143.

No. 12

13   DANSEUSE BLEUE
   Pastel: $21\frac{1}{4} \times 19\frac{3}{4}$ in. (53.9 × 50.1 cm)
   Signed lower left

Colls: Durand-Ruel, Paris; Galerie Thannhauser, Lucerne; Oscar Schmitz,
           Dresden; Wildenstein, London

Exh: Munich, Galerie Thannhauser, 'Degas', July, 1926 (No. 8); Zürich,
           Kunsthaus, 'Collection Oscar Schmitz', 1932 (No. 26); Paris, Galerie
           Wildenstein, 'Collection Oscar Schmitz', 1936 (No. 23); New York,
           Wildenstein, 'Degas', April-May, 1948 (No. 91)

Lit: K. Scheffler in *Künst und Künstler*, 1920-21, repr. 186; M. Dormoy in
           L'Amour de l'Art, 1926, repr. p. 343; J.B. Manson, *The Life and Work of
           Edgar Degas*, 1927, repr. p. 52; *La Collection Oscar Schmitz*, 1936, No. 23,
           repr.; Lemoisne, III, No. 1366; L. Browse, *Degas Dancers*, 1949, No. 186,
           repr.

Painted *c.* 1889.

No. 13

14   FEMME NUE, A GENOUX
    Pastel: $9\frac{1}{2} \times 12\frac{1}{4}$ in. (24.1 × 31.1 cm)
    Facsimile stamp of Degas sale upper left

Colls: Atelier Degas, 2nd Sale, (Lot 212 (1), repr.); Davis, Paris

Lit: Lemoisne, III, No. 1008

Painted *c.* 1889-95.

No. 14

15 MODISTE GARNISSANT UN CHAPEAU

Pastel: 18⅛ × 28 in. (48.2 × 71.1 cm)
Facsimile stamp of the Degas sale lower left

Colls: Atelier Degas, 1st Sale, (Lot 156, repr.); Ambroise Vollard, Paris; Robert Bevan, London

Exh: Edinburgh and London (Arts Council) 'Degas' 1952, (No. 30, pl. IX); London, Wildenstein, 'The French Impressionists and some of their contemporaries', 1963, No. 17, repr.

Lit: Lemoisne, III, No. 1110; *The Connoisseur*, October, 1962, p. 113, repr.

Painted in 1891-95. No. 15 may be compared with a pastel of the same subject, Lemoisne, III, No. 1318.

No. 15

16 LE PETIT DEJEUNER APRES LE BAIN (LA TASSE DU CAFE)
Pastel: 39½ × 27½ in. (100 × 69.8 cm)
Facsimile stamp of the Degas sale lower left

Colls: Atelier Degas, 1st Sale, (Lot 198, repr.); J. Seligmann, Paris; Sir Alfred Chester-Beatty, Dublin; Arthur Tooth and Sons, London

Lit: Lemoisne, III, No. 1150

Painted *c.* 1894. There is a related version, also in pastel, Lemoisne, III, No. 1151.

No. 16

17   FEMME SE COIFFANT
   Pastel: $29\frac{1}{4}$ × 25 in. (74.2 × 63.5 cm)
   Signed lower right

Colls: Ambroise Vollard, Paris; R. de Galea, Paris; Martinez, Paris

Painted *c*. 1895.

No. 17

18　LA TOILETTE

Pastel: 24 × 19$\frac{3}{4}$ in. (60.9 × 50.1 cm)

Signed lower right

Colls:　A. Vollard, Paris; Arthur Tooth and Sons, London; Vivien Leigh, London

Exh:　Edinburgh and London, 'Degas', 1952, (No. 37); London, Arthur Tooth and Sons, 'Recent Acquisitions', November-December, 1949, (No. 16, repr.)

Lit:　Ambroise Vollard, *Album Degas*, 1914, pl. 11; Lemoisne, III, No. 1292

Painted *c.* 1897. No. 18 is a study for, or a replica of, Lemoisne, III, No. 1290.

No. 18

19   BEFORE THE PERFORMANCE
  Canvas: 18$\frac{3}{4}$ × 24$\frac{3}{4}$ in. (47.6 × 62.8 cm)
  Facsimile signature stamp of Degas sale lower right

Colls: Atelier Degas, 1st Sale, (Lot 77, repr.); J. Seligmann, Paris; Captain Edward
       Molyneux, Paris; Lord Eccles, London; Arthur Tooth and Sons, London;
       Alexander Maitland, Edinburgh

Exh: London, Agnew 'Degas', 1936 (No. 8); Edinburgh and London, (Arts
       Council); 'Degas' 1952 (No. 36)

Lit: Lemoisne, III (No. 1261); L. Browse, *Degas Dancers*, 1949 pl. vi; *The
       Maitland Gift and Related Pictures*, National Gallery of Scotland, 1963
       (Ref. No. 224) p. 25, repr.; L. Browse, in *Apollo*, LXXXV, February, 1967,
       pl. I

Painted *c.* 1896-98. Degas did a pastel of a similar composition, see 1st Degas Sale,
(Lot 122); cp. also Lot 190 in the 4th Sale.

Lent by the National Gallery of Scotland, Edinburgh (Maitland Gift).

No. 19

20 FEMME NUE S'ESSUYANT
  Black Chalk: $28\frac{3}{4} \times 22\frac{7}{8}$ in. (73 $\times$ 57.7 cm)
  Facsimile of studio stamp, lower left

Colls: Atelier Degas, 1st Sale (Lot 333 repr.); G. Viau, Paris; his sale 11-12-1942
      (Lot 49 repr. pl. V)

Painted *c.* 1900. Degas painted this theme on many occasions. No. 20 seems to be
a story for a pastel once in the Thorsten-Laurin Collection, Stockholm, repr., P. A.
Lemoisne, *Degas et son oeuvre*, 1954. between pp. 152 and 154.

No. 20

21   STUDY FOR ETUDE DE NU (also called: *Femme à son lever-La Boulangère*)
     Pastel: 30¾ × 19¾ in. (78.1 × 50.1 cm)

Colls: René de Gas, Paris; Maurice de Gas, Paris; Paul Brame, Paris; Reid and
           Lefevre, London

Lit: R. Pickvance in *Apollo*, LXXXIII, January, 1966, Fig. 8

Painted *c.* 1900. This is a variant of *La Boulangère* in the collection of Madame
David-Weill, Paris (Lemoisne, II, 877). R. Pickvance sees a connection with the
Dancer at Rest with hands behind her back, right leg forward, Rewald, No. XXIII.

No. 21

22   QUATRE DANSEUSES
Pastel: 25 × 16 in. (63.5 × 40.6 cm)
Facsimile of Signature stamp, lower left

Colls: Atelier Degas, 1st Sale (Lot 177, repr.) Kahn, Paris; Percy Moore Turner, London; Private collection, Scotland; Private collection, Switzerland

Lit: Ambroise Vollard, *Album Degas*, 1914, pl. XI; Lemoisne, III. No. 1417

Painted *c.* 1902. No. 22 is a companion to another pastel, *Danseuses en Bleu* (Lemoisne, III, No. 1416). He also lists two drawings in the Degas Sale (3rd Sale, Lot 79, and 4th Sale, Lot 150), and a drawing in the Vollard *Album Degas*, pl. XL.

No. 22   65

23   CHEVAL A L'ABREUVOIR
   Bronze 6$\frac{3}{8}$ in. (16 cm)

Lit: Rewald, II. Bronze No. 13

Rewald notes that No. 23 was apparently used by Degas as a model for the horse in his composition *Mademoiselle Fiocre dans le Ballet 'Le Source'* (Brooklyn Museum of Art, Lemoisne No. 146), painted between 1866 and 1868. No. 23 must therefore have been executed during these years.

No. 23

24 CHEVAL MARCHANT A PAS RELEVE
Bronze $8\frac{7}{8}$ in. (22 cm)

Lit: Rewald IV. Bronze No. 11

Executed *c.* 1865-81.

No. 24

25 CHEVAL AU GALOP SUR LE PIED DROIT
    Bronze $5\frac{1}{4}$ in. (13 cm)

Lit: Rewald VI. Bronze No. 47

Executed *c.* 1865-81.

No. 25

26   CHEVAL SE CABRANT
   Bronze 12$\frac{1}{8}$ in. (30.5 cm)

Lit: Rewald XIII. Bronze No. 4

Executed *c.* 1865-81

No. 26

27   ETUDE DE NU POUR LA DANSEUSE HABILLE
  Bronze: 28½ in. (72 cm)

Lit: Rewald XIC. Bronze No. 56

Executed 1879-80. A drawing for No. 27 as well as a detail from another drawing are illustrated by Rewald p. 58.

No. 27

28 GRAND ARABESQUE, DEUXIEME TEMPS
Bronze: 19 in. (48 cm)

Lit: Rewald XXXVI. Bronze No. 15

Rewald points out that Walter Sickert reported that Degas showed him, in the early 'nineties, in his studio in the rue Victor-Massé, the wax model of No. 28. A drawing of *Two dancers executing a Grande Arabesque* is repr. by Rewald, p. 90.

No. 28

29 GRAND ARABESQUE, TROISIEME TEMPS
Bronze: 15⅞ in. (40 cm)

Lit: Rewald XL. Bronze No. 16

Executed *c.* 1882-95.

The artist executed another bronze of a dancer performing a *Grand Arabesque*, Rewald XXXIX, Bronze No. 60.

No. 29

30 DANSEUSE REGARDANT LA PLANTE DE SON PIED DROIT
   Bronze: 18 in. (45.5 cm)

Lit: Rewald XLV. Bronze No. 40

Executed *c.* 1892-95.

Rewald notes that 'Around 1900 Degas asked the founder Hébrard to make plaster casts from several of his sculptures. It is evident that the artists chose for casting those of his works which he considered finished and also worthwhile to be preserved. Among these were the statuette as well as XLVII and LI. Because these sculptures were cast around 1900, P.A. Lemoisne presumes that they were executed at that time. This seems doubtful however, since Degas had glass cases under which he kept the statuettes for which he cared particularly. He may have done the wax models many years before the actual casting, but it is possible that he confided them to Hébrard'. The original plaster cast is repr. Rewald, p. 100. For a drawing connected with No. 30 see No. 6 in this Exhibition.

31 PREPARATION A LA DANSE, LE PIED DROIT EN AVANT
Bronze: 22 in. (55.5 cm)

Lit: Rewald XLVI. Bronze No. 57

Executed *c.* 1882-95.

No. 31

32 DANCE ESPAGNOLE
   Bronze: 17 in. (43 cm)

Lit: Rewald XLVII. Bronze No. 45

Executed *c.* 1882-95.

For a note on when the plaster cast of No. 32 was made by Hébrard see No. 29.
Two views of the original plaster cast are repr. Rewald, p. 104. Degas made another
cast of a dancer in the same attitude, see Rewald LXVI.

No. 32

33   DANSEUSE HABILLE AU REPOSE, LES MAINS SUR LES REINS, LA
JAMBE DROITE EN AVANT
Bronze: 16$\frac{3}{4}$ in. (42.5 cm)

Lit: Rewald LII. Bronze No. 51

Executed *c.* 1896-1911.

No. 32 is in the same attitude as Rewald **XXII** and **XXIII**. A drawing of *Three Dancers at Rest* is repr. Rewald p. 114.

No. 33

NOTES